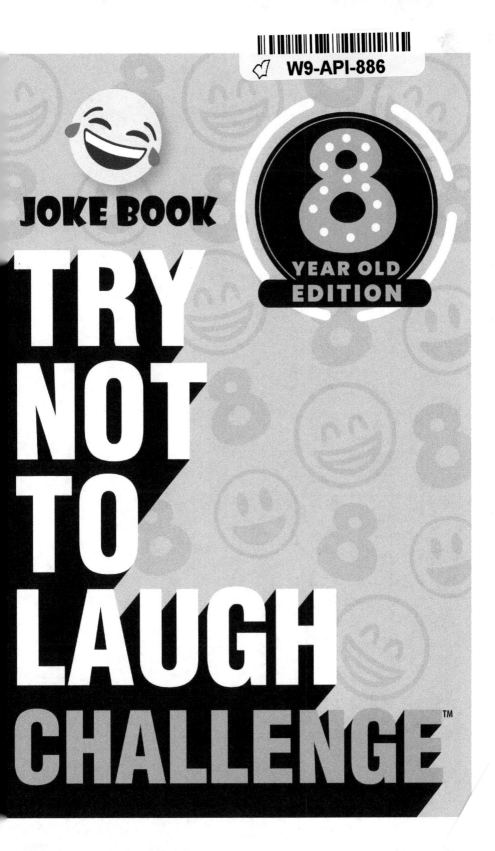

JOKE BOOK

8

YEAR OLD
EDITION

TRY
NOT
TO
LAUGH
CHALLENGE™

Try Not To Laugh Challenge
BONUS PLAY

Join our Joke Club and get the Bonus Play PDF!

Simply send us an email to:

TNTLPublishing@gmail.com

and you will get the following:

- 10 Hilarious, Bonus Jokes
- An entry in our Monthly Giveaway of a $50 Amazon Gift card!

We draw a new winner each month and will contact you via email!

Good luck!

😊

WELCOME TO THE
RY NOT TO LAUGH CHALLENGE!

ULES OF THE GAME:

Grab a friend or family member, a pen/pencil, and your comedic kills! Determine who will be "Jokester 1" and "Jokester 2".

Take turns reading the jokes aloud to each other, and check the ox next to each joke you get a laugh from! Each laugh box is orth 1 point, and the pages are labeled to instruct and guide when is each player's turn.

Once you have both completed telling jokes in the round, tally up our laugh points and mark it down on each score page! There is a otal of 10 Rounds.

Play as many rounds as you like! Once you reach the last round, ound 10, tally up ALL points from the previous rounds to determine ho is the CHAMPION LAUGH MASTER!

★ Round 11 - The Tie-Breaker Round.

n the event of a tie, proceed to Round 11. This round will be Winner Takes All!', so whoever scores more laugh points in this ound alone, is crowned the CHAMPION LAUGH MASTER!

TIP: Use an expressive voice, facial expressions, and even silly ody movement to really get the most out of each joke and keep the crowd laughing!

Now, it's time to play!

ROUND

1

Why was the striped shirt always in disguise?

It didn't want to be spotted!

Why did the wall give everythin it had to charity?

It wanted to be SHELF-less!

What is the soap's least favorite language?

GERM-an.

Why did the drummer have long hair?

Because he really liked BANGS!

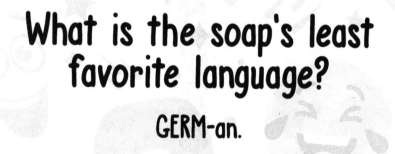

What do you call 1,000 snails going up Mount Everest?

Mountain SLIME-ers!

LAUGH ✓

What kind of tours do ghosts enjoy?

FRIGHT-seeing tours!

LAUGH ☐

Why did the man bring tomato sauce to his hotel room?

He wanted to KETCHUP on sleep!

 LAUGH

What's a traveler's least favorite ice cream?

Rocky Road!

LAUGH ☐

Pass the book to Jokester 2! ➜

11

JOKESTER 2

Why did the piglets go to story hour?

They were ready for pig tales!

What do monkeys love to buy at carnivals?

Baboon balloons!

Where do lizards go for a spa day?

The Iguana Sauna!

What instrument do bison play?

Buffalo banjos!

Why did B lose D?

It couldn't C!

☐ LAUGH

Why did the dentist lose his job?

He was always stretching the tooth!

☐ LAUGH

Why is the little hand on the clock constantly running late?

It's always short on time.

☐ LAUGH

Why did the calendar stay single?

It was always getting the wrong date!

☐ LAUGH

Time to add up your points! →

SCORE BOARD

Add up each Jokester's laugh points
for this round!

JOKESTER 1　　　　$\dfrac{\quad\quad}{\text{Total}}\, /8$

JOKESTER 2　　　　$\dfrac{\quad\quad}{\text{Total}}\, /8$

ROUND WINNER

ROUND
2

Why would a werewolf lose a fight against a vampire?

Their bark is worse than their bite!

Why is Barbie always late?

She likes to get DOLL-ed up!

Why are pumpkins so brave?

They have a lot of GUTS!

Why did the kid put nets in her nose?

She wanted to CATCH a cold!

 **JOKESTER 1**

What did the moon say when the sun got sick?

"You don't look so hot..."

LAUGH

Why was the witch so good at English?

She loved to SPELL!

LAUGH

What's the most talkative flower?

Two-lips. (Tulips)

LAUGH

What did the tree say on their first date?

"Don't get all sappy on me!"

LAUGH

Pass the book to Jokester 2! ➜

What do cows wear to make them invisible?

Cow-MOO-flage!

Why did the bird get sick?

It came down with the FLEW!

Why is food your best friend?

It knows you inside and out!

Why are all carousel horses friends?

They travel in the same circles!

How does the traffic light talk
to the billboard?

With SIGN language!

◻ LAUGH

What do you call an animal
that sells jewelry?

A WATCH dog.

◻ LAUGH

Why did the knife and spoon
pull their car over?

There was a fork in the road!

◻ LAUGH

What happened to the puzzle
when it got upset?

It fell to pieces!

◻ LAUGH

Time to add up your points! →

SCORE BOARD

Add up each Jokester's laugh points for this round!

JOKESTER 1

$\dfrac{\quad}{\text{Total}}$ /8

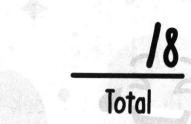

JOKESTER 2

$\dfrac{\quad}{\text{Total}}$ /8

ROUND WINNER

ROUND

3

 **JOKESTER 1**

What is a llama's favorite musical artist?

LLAMA Del Rey!

What is a buck's favorite game?

Truth or Deer!

Which talk show host do birds love?

Jimmy FALCON!

How does a wad of bubblegum travel?

On a chew-chew train!

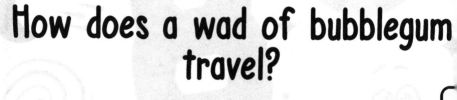

How did the stomper finally say 'no'?

He put his foot down.

⬜ LAUGH

What do you call an amusing leg joint?

⬜ LAUGH

A fun-KNEE! (Funny)

Which birds help construction workers the most?

Cranes.

⬜ LAUGH

I'm in trouble for stealing art, but I didn't do it! I was picture FRAMED.

⬜ LAUGH

Pass the book to Jokester 2! ➜

23

On what holiday do vampires eat turkey?

FANGS-giving!

How do trees make friends?

They branch out!

How do you teach a rose to ride a bike?

Tell it to PETAL!

Mars missed his doctor's appointment. He didn't PLANET right.

Why do most people use the elevator?

STAIR-ing is rude!

☐ LAUGH

How did they know the ocean was kidnapped?

It was all TIDE up!

☐ LAUGH

Where do owls stay on vacation?

In a HOO-tel.

☐ LAUGH

Where do you find a car with no wheels?

Wherever you left it!

☐ LAUGH

Time to add up your points! →

25

SCORE BOARD

Add up each Jokester's laugh points for this round!

JOKESTER 1 $\dfrac{}{\text{Total}}$ /8

JOKESTER 2 $\dfrac{}{\text{Total}}$ /8

ROUND WINNER

ROUND
4

What shoes does a ninja wear?

SNEAK-ers.

What's a rabbit's favorite year

Leap year!

What do you call it when elephants go to the pool?

Swimming trunks.

Why was the singer so sweaty during her performance?

She had no fans!

JOKESTER 1

What type of accessory does a comedian wear?

A watch, so their timing is always perfect.

 LAUGH

What does Washington D.C. taste like?

Monu-MINTS!

LAUGH

Why shouldn't you play music to the clouds?

They'll dance up a storm!

LAUGH

Did you hear about the lightbulb that never studies for tests?

It's not very bright.

LAUGH

Pass the book to Jokester 2! ➔

How do you fight ocean sickness?

Take vitamin SEA!

What's Santa's favorite place to go while on vacation?

The Gift shops!

What do you call a surprised electrician?

Shocked!

What made the toilet so good at poker?

It had a lot of flushes!

 **JOKESTER 2**

What did the birthday cake want at the noisey party?

Just a little peace. (Piece)　　◯ LAUGH

What did the tree say, when asked if it was willing to take a test to see what it's made of?

"I wood."　　◯ LAUGH

took a vacation to the world's windiest town. It really blew me away!

◯ LAUGH

Why couldn't the car afford repairs?

It was BROKE.　　◯ LAUGH

Time to add up your points! ➔

31

SCORE BOARD

Add up each Jokester's laugh points for this round!

JOKESTER 1

$\dfrac{\quad\quad}{\text{Total}}$ /8

JOKESTER 2

$\dfrac{\quad\quad}{\text{Total}}$ /8

ROUND WINNER

ROUND
5

What kind of tape is never sticky?

Measuring tape!

How do you make it to the library right before they close.

You BOOK it.

What kind of shoes do plumber's wear?

Clogs.

My friend got frustrated and wanted to rip his homework. I told him that's a TEAR-able idea

What do you call a boat you just bought?

A Ca-NEW!

LAUGH

What's so great about a rubber band's schedule?

It's always flexible!

LAUGH

Why were the Kleenex's feet cold?

It didn't have any tis-shoes.

LAUGH

What is the box's favorite snack?

Packing peanuts.

LAUGH

Pass the book to Jokester 2! →

What do you call an animal that loves to work out?

A BUFF-alo!

What is a deer's favorite breakfast?

DOE-nuts!

Why was the horse late?

It kept STALL-ing!

What is an owl's favorite book?

'Horton Hears a HOO.'

Knock knock.
Who's there?
Norway.
Norway, who?
Norway am I going to tell you
unless you open the door!

LAUGH

What kind of boats can you
find in a dining room?

Gravy boats!

LAUGH

What animal is always warm?

A WOOL-verine!

LAUGH

What is a turtle's favorite candy?

Anything with a hard shell!

LAUGH

Time to add up your points! →

37

SCORE BOARD

Add up each Jokester's laugh points for this round!

JOKESTER 1

$$\frac{/8}{\text{Total}}$$

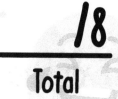

JOKESTER 2

$$\frac{/8}{\text{Total}}$$

ROUND WINNER

ROUND
6

Why did the cactus get straight A's?

It was very SHARP!

What do you call a plant that you can fit in your hands?

A Palm Tree.

Why is it so hard to have a conversation with an astronaut?

They always space out!

Why was the sun so famous?

Well, it is a super-STAR!

What does the shop owner say, when a customer with excellent taste is on their way out the door?

"Good buy!"

◯ LAUGH

Why did the storm lock itself inside?

It didn't want to get rained out.

◯ LAUGH

What's a rainbow's favorite reading material?

Coloring books!

◯ LAUGH

Why do squares work out?

To get in SHAPE!

◯ LAUGH

Pass the book to Jokester 2! ➔

What's a gardener's favorite inside past-time?

LAWN-dry!

How do you propose to a fish?

Offer them a RING-worm!

What's the best bone to break?

The wishbone, of course!

What do penguins wear to business meetings?

Their black and white suit!

 **JOKESTER 2**

How do you get fit at work?

DESK-ercise!

☐ LAUGH

What do you use to create graffiti in a church?

PRAY paint!

☐ LAUGH

What do you call it when you take a nap before dinner?

A NAP-petizer.

☐ LAUGH

What is the fastest part of a pencil?

The e-RACE-er!

☐ LAUGH

Time to add up your points! →

SCORE BOARD

Add up each Jokester's laugh points for this round!

JOKESTER 1 $\dfrac{/8}{\text{Total}}$

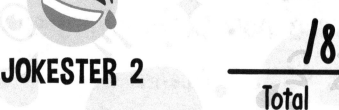

JOKESTER 2 $\dfrac{/8}{\text{Total}}$

ROUND WINNER

ROUND
7

 **JOKESTER 1**

Why was the train annoying to its colleagues?

It whistled while it worked!

What sport do numbers enjoy most?

TEN-nis!

What did the cake pan say to the eggs?

"Batter up!"

What do you call a monkey on an airplane?

A flying monkey!

Why did the skeleton stop drinking soda?

It went right through him!

LAUGH

What bug do knights like the least?

A DRAGON-fly!

LAUGH

Where does a Yeti keep its money?

In a snow bank.

LAUGH

Why did the pirate have a peg leg?

He was de-FEET-ed in battle!

LAUGH

Pass the book to Jokester 2! ➔

What do you call a storm of cats?

A FUR-icane!

Why can't you trust the Invisible Man?

You can see right through him!

Why was the zookeeper fired?

He was always LION down on the job!

What do you call a poorly behaved owl?

A HOO-ligan!

Why were the shorts out of breath?

They were always PANT-ing.

LAUGH

Why can't the car hangout with the airplanes?

It's not fly enough!

LAUGH

Why is the circle never serious?

It's always kidding a-ROUND.

LAUGH

What do you call the leader of the lights?

'The Headlamp.'

LAUGH

Time to add up your points! →

SCORE BOARD

Add up each Jokester's laugh points for this round!

JOKESTER 1
$$\frac{}{\text{Total}}\ /8$$

JOKESTER 2
$$\frac{}{\text{Total}}\ /8$$

ROUND WINNER

ROUND 8

Why did the glass break after laughing?

He was cracking up!

What is the mattress' favorite season?

Spring.

What's the burrito's favorite game?

BEAN-go!

What does a mountain say if yo ask it a question about the ocean?

"I'm not SHORE."

 **JOKESTER 1**

What do soccer players say when they want to hang out?

"Let's KICK it."

LAUGH ☐

What's a leprechaun's favorite meal?

Lucky Charms!

LAUGH ☐

What superhero loves dinner time?

SUPPER Man.

LAUGH ☐

What is a rubber duck's favorite sport?

BATH-ketball!

LAUGH ☐

Pass the book to Jokester 2! →

What do you call a bunny who carries your luggage?

The bell-HOP!

How does the doctor make your mouth sad?

She uses a tongue depressor.

What insect just wants to be left alone?

A lettuce bee!

Why do phones get married so often?

They are always giving people RINGS.

54

 **JOKESTER 2**

What do flowers call their closest friends?

Best Buds.

○ LAUGH

Why was the baseball always so happy?

It was in g-LOVE!

○ LAUGH

Why are runners so good at paying attention?

They like to stay on TRACK.

○ LAUGH

What do you call it when you get pranked by a panda?

Getting BAMBOO-zled.

○ LAUGH

Time to add up your points! →

SCORE BOARD

Add up each Jokester's laugh points for this round!

JOKESTER 1 /8
———————
Total

JOKESTER 2 /8
———————
Total

ROUND WINNER

ROUND
9

How do you insult an onion?

Call them a cry baby!

Why was the Dorito getting their car fixed?

The windshield was CHIP-ped!

What's the friendliest attractio at a waterpark?

The WAVE-pool!

What did the pants say, when asked if the store was open?

"Sorry, we're CLOTHES."

 **JOKESTER 1**

Where do you put snow that's not yours?

Frost and Found!

What do you call a can of soda rafting down the river?

A Root Beer Float!

Why couldn't the gnome go out to play with his friends?

He had too much GNOME-work!

What night of the year does everyone put on stilts?

TALL-oween!

Pass the book to Jokester 2! →

How did Peter Pan cross the large ocean channel?

He took a ferry! (Fairy)

Why was the vehicle feeling so hot?

It was car sick!

Where do ghosts catch their planes?

At the SCARE-port!

Which state sounds like a small soft drink?

Minne-SODA. (Minnesota)

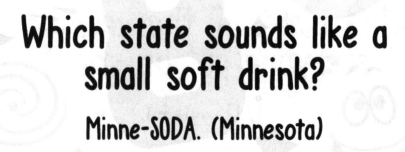

Why did the flower win an award?

Because she ROSE to the occasion!

LAUGH

Why was the car held back in school?

He'd lost his DRIVE to advance.

LAUGH

Why was the thermometer angry at the fever?

They'd just had a heated encounter.

LAUGH

I went to the squirrel's house for dinner last night and it was delicious. We had ACORN-on-the-cob!

LAUGH

Time to add up your points! →

SCORE BOARD

Add up each Jokester's laugh points for this round!

JOKESTER 1 $\dfrac{}{\text{Total}}$ /8

JOKESTER 2 $\dfrac{}{\text{Total}}$ /8

ROUND WINNER

ROUND
10

What do you call a couple, who both play the bells?

'Partners in Chime.'

What kind of dressing do cowboys like?

RANCH dressing!

Do you know how to make rose-flavored cookies?

Just add a cup of flower. (Flour)

Why did the chicken live on the hilltop?

She wanted to make egg rolls!

JOKESTER 1

What kind of magical creature helps give the meaning of words?

A Diction-Fairy.

○ LAUGH

Why did the glue hire a lawyer?

It was in a sticky situation.

○ LAUGH

Which two states have the best Christmas music?

The CAROL-inas!

○ LAUGH

How do you find the king's son?

Follow the foot-PRINCE! (Footprints)

○ LAUGH

Pass the book to Jokester 2! ⟶

What is a cat's favorite sport?

Hairball.

What was the alligator's excuse for not calling back?

He was too swamped!

The wasp is having trouble making friends. I told him to jus BEE himself!

Which monster is known for being the most confused?

A Where Wolf?!

Why did the amateur baker put Pepsi in the oven?

He needed some baking soda!

☐ LAUGH

What vegetable is the best drummer?

The BEET! (Beat)

☐ LAUGH

How did the hammer do on its test?

Nailed it!

☐ LAUGH

What city is home to the most worms?

The Big Apple!

☐ LAUGH

Time to add up your points! →

SCORE BOARD

Add up each Jokester's laugh points for this round!

JOKESTER 1   /8
_____
Total

JOKESTER 2   /8
_____
Total

ROUND WINNER

Add up all your points from each round.
e Jokester with the most points is crowned

The Laugh Master!

the event of a tie, continue to Round 11
- The Tie-Breaker Round!

JOKESTER 1

_____
Grand Total

JOKESTER 2

_____
Grand Total

_____
THE LAUGH MASTER

ROUND

11

TIE-BREAKER
(Winner Takes ALL!)

JOKESTER 1

What is an astronaut's favorite drink?

Gravi-TEA.

Why did all the fish swim to th bottom of the lake?

They heard it was fishing season!

What's the best sport to watch while moving?

BOX-ing!

What's a baseball player's favorite instrument?

The Base. (Bass)

 **JOKESTER 1**

Knock Knock.
Who's there?
Java.
Java, who?
Java a dollar?
I want to buy a candy bar!

☐ LAUGH

Where do numbers take a bath?

In a math tub!

☐ LAUGH

What do you call an insect that complains a lot?

A GRUMBLE-bee!

☐ LAUGH

Which monument is in the biggest hurry?

Mount RUSH-more!

☐ LAUGH

Pass the book to Jokester 2! →

My sheets put themselves on my bed yesterday. I offered to help, but they said they had it COVERED!

Why did the fog stay in town?

Because it MIST its flight!

What do you call a tree with a broken heart?

A Weeping Willow.

Where is the best place to sleep in a truck?

The bed!

Why should you knit socks
for your soulmate?

To show that you're thread over heels!

LAUGH

What is the national
anthem of monkeys?

The Star-Spangled Banana.

LAUGH

Knock Knock.
Who's there?
Goat.
Goat, who?
Goat to the Grand Canyon.
It's awesome!

LAUGH

What state is always sneezing?

Mass-ACHOO-setts!

LAUGH

Time to add up your points! →

Add up all your points from the
Tie-Breaker Round.
The Jokester with the most points is crown

The Laugh Master!

JOKESTER 1

$/8$

Total

JOKESTER 2

$/8$

Total

THE LAUGH MASTER

Check out our

Visit our Amazon Store at:

other joke books!